Speaking A Volume Up

Set In Soul

© 2020 Tatiana Media LLC in partnership with Set In Soul LLC

ISBN #: 978-1-949874-96-9

Published by Tatiana Media LLC

For general information on our other products and services, please contact our Customer Support within the United States at support@setinsoul.com.

Tatiana Media LLC as well as Set In Soul LLC publishes its books in a variety of electronic formats. Some content that appears in print may not be available in electronic books.

This Journal Belongs To

_____

Dedicated To My Heart And My Spirit. It's Just Time For Me To Speak Up.

Table Of Contents

How To Use This Journal

There are moments in life where discernment must be used as to when one should speak up and take a stand on a subject. But if you find that there are too many moments where you should have spoken up but didn't, then something must change. There may have been some moments in the past where not speaking up has affected how you feel about yourself and has created uncomfortable and/or unwanted situations you are currently in. If over time you find that you are unable to assert yourself, allow others to speak over you, take advantage of you and as a result tear down your self-esteem ... then it is time to learn how to communicate confidently without the fear of what others think. No more being timid, docile or pushing your feelings to the side because of the fear of the result.

Now that you realized that things must change and you would like to be treated with respect you must learn to be assertive. Your voice and feelings matter. It is important to be able to express your needs and wants regardless of the terrifying feelings that come with it. This journal helps you to build up your mental and emotional muscles that are needed to stand up and speak up for yourself as well as get to the root of what has been keeping you from expressing what you believe is right. It is time to understand why you behave the way you do in certain situations and why you silence your voice with certain people. By doing this you will start to become more of your own best friend and even your strongest ally. Through standing up for yourself you will begin to learn to treat yourself with love, understanding and compassion. Speaking up for yourself is not just a tough thing to do but mainly the right thing to do. The more that you start speaking up for yourself at the right times the better you will become at expressing your thoughts, feelings and concerns to the right people. You begin to understand that speaking up for yourself is an essential part of self-nurturance.

We recommend using this journal every morning and night. Your answers may be different each day and over time you will notice your growth in your confidence about the things you choose to speak up and out about. This is your time to try to gain insight into your emotional processes that you may experience when it is time to speak up. Be specific. Identify exactly how each situation went. Identify your thoughts. Identify your emotions. Identify your behavior. What did you think? How did you feel? Did you feel tense? Did you feel sick to your stomach? Did you feel frightened? Be factual and honest. Reflect on your responses then ask yourself what would have been a better and more assertive way to respond. Visualize how you should have behaved and what you should have said to stand up for yourself. Writing about your experiences helps to reduce the intensity of the negative emotions that you feel about you. You'll begin to see that you don't have to be afraid or intimidated to speak up. The motivational quotes throughout this journal are there to encourage you along your journey to finding your voice and using it. For the people who you want to hear, receive and take an action on your message right now who haven't been able to hear you in the past, we want you to practice your ability to speak a volume up. So, let's get started.

My Old Voice

My Old Voice

I Believe I Am:

I Have A Hard Time:

When I Speak, I Believe People Are:

What Is My Communication Style?

When Other People Are Speaking, I Am Always Thinking:

My Old Voice

When I Am Talking, I Am Always Thinking:

I Have A Hard Time Speaking Up About:

I Believe It Is Hard For Me To Stand Up For Myself Because:

My Ideal Way To Solve Problems:

I Always Find Myself:

My Old Voice

I Feel Like If I Stand Up For Myself I Will Lose:

I Feel Like If I Stand Up For Myself I Will Gain:

I Stopped Speaking Up For Myself At The Age Of:

I Stopped Speaking Up For Myself When I Saw:

I Stopped Speaking Up For Myself When:

My Old Voice

Speaking Up Is Not Worth:

Speaking Up Is Worth:

What I Have Lost By Not Speaking Up:

What I Have Gained By Not Speaking Up:

I Use My Voice:

My Old Voice

I Want To Speak Up About:

When I See Other People Speak Up For Themselves, I Feel:

I Believe That When I Do Not Speak Up For Myself:

I Always Think:

I Am Afraid:

My Old Voice

I Want To Be Viewed As:

I Respect Myself For:

A List Of What I Have To Offer:

I Currently Care About:

What I Should Not Care About That I Currently Do:

My Old Voice

My Friends Believe:

In What Ways Am I Assertive?

Do I Believe Other Peoples' Wants Are More Important Than Mine?

In What Ways Do I Sacrifice?

Do I Make My Wants And/Or Needs Known?

My Old Voice

When I Talk, I Believe People Hear:

In Intimate Relationships, I Have A Hard Time Speaking Up About:

At Work, I Have A Hard Time Speaking Up About:

With My Doctor, I Have A Hard Time Speaking Up About:

With My Family, I Have A Hard Time Speaking Up About:

My Old Voice

It Is Easier To Tell My Truth When:

I Like To Avoid:

Overtime, Not Speaking Up For Myself Has Caused Me:

I Feel Like:

I Am Tired Of:

My Old Voice

I Want To Start:

I Want To Stop:

In The Past, I Have Stood Up For Myself About:

I Would Like To Be More Assertive With:

As Of Today, I Would Like To Be:

My Old Voice

I Will No Longer Be Afraid:

I Realized That:

What Does Standing Up For Myself Look Like?

How Do I Teach People How To Treat Me?

How Do I Establish Boundaries?

My Old Voice

What Are One Of My Boundaries?

How Would I Like To Verbally Communicate My Thoughts:

The Last Time I Spoke Up For Myself, I Felt:

The Last Time I Spoke Up For Myself, The Result Was:

The Last Time I Spoke Up For Myself, I Did Not Like:

My Old Voice

Negative Thoughts That Come Up When I Speak Up For Myself:

I Do Not Want To Be Seen As:

Other People's Thoughts About Me Are:

I Am Now Willing To:

What Is Really Bothering Me?

My Old Voice

When Do I Feel Like I Can Assert Myself?

When Is The Best Time To Express An Opinion?

What Kinds Of Questions Am I Afraid To Ask?

What Kinds Of Questions Do I Want To Ask?

What Is Acceptable Behavior While Communicating?

My Old Voice

Being Dismissed Feels:

Being Demeaned Feels:

Being Ostracized Feels:

To Lose Something I Want Because I Spoke Up Feels:

Do I Feel The Need To Defuse Volatile Situations By Ignoring What Is Best For Me?

My Old Voice

What Is My Body Language When I Try To Speak Up For Myself?

What Is My Body Language When I Try To Speak Up For Others?

When Do I Say No?

Why Do I Care About The Outcome From Speaking Out?

What Is The Best Way To Address An Issue?

My Old Voice

How Do I Stand Up To One Family Member For Another?

The Best Way I Prepare Myself To Speak Up In Uncomfortable Situations:

No Longer Will I Take Responsibility For?

Why Is It Important For Me To Speak My Peace?

I Want To Be:

My Old Voice

I Always:

No Longer Will I Give In To:

I Always Said:

It Is A New Day:

I Wish I Spoke Up About It

I Wish I Spoke Up About (Write Down The Person/Issue And The Result/s From Not Speaking Up That Has Changed Things And/Or You)....

I Wish I Spoke Up About (Write Down The Person/Issue And The Result/s From Not Speaking Up That Has Changed Things And/Or You)....

I Wish I Spoke Up About (Write Down The Person/Issue And The Result/s From Not Speaking Up That Has Changed Things And/Or You)....

I Wish I Spoke Up About (Write Down The Person/Issue And The Result/s From Not Speaking Up That Has Changed Things And/Or You)....

I Wish I Spoke Up About (Write Down The Person/Issue And The Result/s From Not Speaking Up That Has Changed Things And/Or You)....

I Wish I Spoke Up About (Write Down The Person/Issue And The Result/s From Not Speaking Up That Has Changed Things And/Or You)....

I Wish I Spoke Up About (Write Down The Person/Issue And The Result/s From Not Speaking Up That Has Changed Things And/Or You)....

I Wish I Spoke Up About (Write Down The Person/Issue And The Result/s From Not Speaking Up That Has Changed Things And/Or You)....

I Wish I Spoke Up About (Write Down The Person/Issue And The Result/s From Not Speaking Up That Has Changed Things And/Or You)....

I Wish I Spoke Up About (Write Down The Person/Issue And The Result/s From Not Speaking Up That Has Changed Things And/Or You)....

Speaking Up Daily

Speaking Up Daily
Morning Thoughts

Date:

I Feel:

What Is On My Mind This Morning?

Today I Have Peace In Knowing:

Today I Will Have The Courage To Say:

I Am Declaring:

Evening Thoughts

How Did I Speak Up For Myself Today?

I Feel Good Now That I:

Today I Asked:

Today I No Longer Feared:

Based On My Response To The Previous Prompt, The Result Was:

Today It Made Me Feel Good To Complete This Conversation:

I Let Go Of The Fear:

Today I Responded The Way My Spirit Wanted To By:

Today I Set The Boundary:

Speaking Up Daily

Morning Thoughts

Date:

What Is On My Mind This
Morning?

Today I Will Have The Courage To
Say:

I Feel:

Today I Have Peace In Knowing:

I Am Declaring:

Evening Thoughts

How Did I Speak Up For Myself
Today?

Today I Asked:

Based On My Response To The
Previous Prompt, The Result Was:

I Let Go Of The Fear:

Today I Set The Boundary:

I Feel Good Now That I:

Today I No Longer Feared:

Today It Made Me Feel Good To
Complete This Conversation:

Today I Responded The Way My
Spirit Wanted To By:

Speaking Up Daily

Morning Thoughts

Date:

I Feel:

What Is On My Mind This Morning?

Today I Have Peace In Knowing:

Today I Will Have The Courage To Say:

I Am Declaring:

Evening Thoughts

How Did I Speak Up For Myself Today?

I Feel Good Now That I:

Today I Asked:

Today I No Longer Feared:

Based On My Response To The Previous Prompt, The Result Was:

Today It Made Me Feel Good To Complete This Conversation:

I Let Go Of The Fear:

Today I Responded The Way My Spirit Wanted To By:

Today I Set The Boundary:

What I Have To Say Has Value.

I Can Walk
Away
Knowing That
I Said What
I Have Been
Holding In.

Speaking Up Daily

Morning Thoughts

Date: I Feel:

What Is On My Mind This
Morning?
                                         Today I Have Peace In Knowing:

Today I Will Have The Courage To
Say: I Am Declaring:

Evening Thoughts

How Did I Speak Up For Myself
Today?
                                         I Feel Good Now That I:

Today I Asked: Today I No Longer Feared:

Based On My Response To The   Today It Made Me Feel Good To
Previous Prompt, The Result Was: Complete This Conversation:

I Let Go Of The Fear: Today I Responded The Way My
                                         Spirit Wanted To By:

Today I Set The Boundary:

Speaking Up Daily
Morning Thoughts

Date:

What Is On My Mind This
Morning?

Today I Will Have The Courage To
Say:

I Feel:

Today I Have Peace In Knowing:

I Am Declaring:

Evening Thoughts

How Did I Speak Up For Myself
Today?

Today I Asked:

Based On My Response To The
Previous Prompt, The Result Was:

I Let Go Of The Fear:

Today I Set The Boundary:

I Feel Good Now That I:

Today I No Longer Feared:

Today It Made Me Feel Good To
Complete This Conversation:

Today I Responded The Way My
Spirit Wanted To By:

Speaking Up Daily

Morning Thoughts

Date:

I Feel:

What Is On My Mind This Morning?

Today I Have Peace In Knowing:

Today I Will Have The Courage To Say:

I Am Declaring:

Evening Thoughts

How Did I Speak Up For Myself Today?

I Feel Good Now That I:

Today I Asked:

Today I No Longer Feared:

Based On My Response To The Previous Prompt, The Result Was:

Today It Made Me Feel Good To Complete This Conversation:

I Let Go Of The Fear:

Today I Responded The Way My Spirit Wanted To By:

Today I Set The Boundary:

I Am Not Afraid To Stand Up For Myself.

My Thoughts Out Loud

Speaking Up Daily

Morning Thoughts

Date: | I Feel:

What Is On My Mind This Morning? | Today I Have Peace In Knowing:

Today I Will Have The Courage To Say: | I Am Declaring:

Evening Thoughts

How Did I Speak Up For Myself Today? | I Feel Good Now That I:

Today I Asked: | Today I No Longer Feared:

Based On My Response To The Previous Prompt, The Result Was: | Today It Made Me Feel Good To Complete This Conversation:

I Let Go Of The Fear: | Today I Responded The Way My Spirit Wanted To By:

Today I Set The Boundary:

Speaking Up Daily

Morning Thoughts

Date: I Feel:

What Is On My Mind This   Today I Have Peace In Knowing:
Morning?

Today I Will Have The Courage To   I Am Declaring:
Say:

Evening Thoughts

How Did I Speak Up For Myself   I Feel Good Now That I:
Today?

Today I Asked: Today I No Longer Feared:

Based On My Response To The   Today It Made Me Feel Good To
Previous Prompt, The Result Was: Complete This Conversation:

I Let Go Of The Fear: Today I Responded The Way My
                                         Spirit Wanted To By:

Today I Set The Boundary:

Every Time That I Speak Up For Myself, I....

Speaking Up Daily

Morning Thoughts

Date: I Feel:

What Is On My Mind This   Today I Have Peace In Knowing:
Morning?

Today I Will Have The Courage To   I Am Declaring:
Say:

Evening Thoughts

How Did I Speak Up For Myself   I Feel Good Now That I:
Today?

Today I Asked: Today I No Longer Feared:

Based On My Response To The   Today It Made Me Feel Good To
Previous Prompt, The Result Was: Complete This Conversation:

I Let Go Of The Fear: Today I Responded The Way My
                                     Spirit Wanted To By:

Today I Set The Boundary:

Speaking Up Daily
Morning Thoughts

Date: I Feel:

What Is On My Mind This   Today I Have Peace In Knowing:
Morning?

Today I Will Have The Courage To   I Am Declaring:
Say:

Evening Thoughts

How Did I Speak Up For Myself   I Feel Good Now That I:
Today?

Today I Asked: Today I No Longer Feared:

Based On My Response To The   Today It Made Me Feel Good To
Previous Prompt, The Result Was: Complete This Conversation:

I Let Go Of The Fear: Today I Responded The Way My
                                    Spirit Wanted To By:

Today I Set The Boundary:

My Thoughts Out Loud

Speaking Up Daily

Morning Thoughts

Date:

What Is On My Mind This
Morning?

Today I Will Have The Courage To
Say:

I Feel:

Today I Have Peace In Knowing:

I Am Declaring:

Evening Thoughts

How Did I Speak Up For Myself
Today?

Today I Asked:

Based On My Response To The
Previous Prompt, The Result Was:

I Let Go Of The Fear:

Today I Set The Boundary:

I Feel Good Now That I:

Today I No Longer Feared:

Today It Made Me Feel Good To
Complete This Conversation:

Today I Responded The Way My
Spirit Wanted To By:

My Feelings Matter.

I Will Always Stand Up For Myself.

Speaking Up Daily

Morning Thoughts

Date: I Feel:

What Is On My Mind This   Today I Have Peace In Knowing:
Morning?

Today I Will Have The Courage To   I Am Declaring:
Say:

Evening Thoughts

How Did I Speak Up For Myself   I Feel Good Now That I:
Today?

Today I Asked: Today I No Longer Feared:

Based On My Response To The   Today It Made Me Feel Good To
Previous Prompt, The Result Was: Complete This Conversation:

I Let Go Of The Fear: Today I Responded The Way My
                                         Spirit Wanted To By:

Today I Set The Boundary:

Speaking Up Daily

Morning Thoughts

Date:

I Feel:

What Is On My Mind This Morning?

Today I Have Peace In Knowing:

Today I Will Have The Courage To Say:

I Am Declaring:

Evening Thoughts

How Did I Speak Up For Myself Today?

I Feel Good Now That I:

Today I Asked:

Today I No Longer Feared:

Based On My Response To The Previous Prompt, The Result Was:

Today It Made Me Feel Good To Complete This Conversation:

I Let Go Of The Fear:

Today I Responded The Way My Spirit Wanted To By:

Today I Set The Boundary:

Speaking Up Daily

Morning Thoughts

Date:

I Feel:

What Is On My Mind This Morning?

Today I Have Peace In Knowing:

Today I Will Have The Courage To Say:

I Am Declaring:

Evening Thoughts

How Did I Speak Up For Myself Today?

I Feel Good Now That I:

Today I Asked:

Today I No Longer Feared:

Based On My Response To The Previous Prompt, The Result Was:

Today It Made Me Feel Good To Complete This Conversation:

I Let Go Of The Fear:

Today I Responded The Way My Spirit Wanted To By:

Today I Set The Boundary:

When I See Other People Speaking Up For Themselves, I Feel....

My Thoughts Out Loud

Speaking Up Daily

Morning Thoughts

Date:

I Feel:

What Is On My Mind This Morning?

Today I Have Peace In Knowing:

Today I Will Have The Courage To Say:

I Am Declaring:

Evening Thoughts

How Did I Speak Up For Myself Today?

I Feel Good Now That I:

Today I Asked:

Today I No Longer Feared:

Based On My Response To The Previous Prompt, The Result Was:

Today It Made Me Feel Good To Complete This Conversation:

I Let Go Of The Fear:

Today I Responded The Way My Spirit Wanted To By:

Today I Set The Boundary:

Speaking Up Daily

Morning Thoughts

Date:

I Feel:

What Is On My Mind This
Morning?

Today I Have Peace In Knowing:

Today I Will Have The Courage To
Say:

I Am Declaring:

Evening Thoughts

How Did I Speak Up For Myself
Today?

I Feel Good Now That I:

Today I Asked:

Today I No Longer Feared:

Based On My Response To The
Previous Prompt, The Result Was:

Today It Made Me Feel Good To
Complete This Conversation:

I Let Go Of The Fear:

Today I Responded The Way My
Spirit Wanted To By:

Today I Set The Boundary:

I Will Speak My Mind Even When I Am Scared.

People In My Family Who Have No Problems Speaking Up For Themselves....

Speaking Up Daily

Morning Thoughts

Date:

What Is On My Mind This
Morning?

Today I Will Have The Courage To
Say:

I Feel:

Today I Have Peace In Knowing:

I Am Declaring:

Evening Thoughts

How Did I Speak Up For Myself
Today?

Today I Asked:

Based On My Response To The
Previous Prompt, The Result Was:

I Let Go Of The Fear:

Today I Set The Boundary:

I Feel Good Now That I:

Today I No Longer Feared:

Today It Made Me Feel Good To
Complete This Conversation:

Today I Responded The Way My
Spirit Wanted To By:

My Thoughts Out Loud

Speaking Up Daily

Morning Thoughts

Date:

What Is On My Mind This
Morning?

Today I Will Have The Courage To
Say:

I Feel:

Today I Have Peace In Knowing:

I Am Declaring:

Evening Thoughts

How Did I Speak Up For Myself
Today?

Today I Asked:

Based On My Response To The
Previous Prompt, The Result Was:

I Let Go Of The Fear:

Today I Set The Boundary:

I Feel Good Now That I:

Today I No Longer Feared:

Today It Made Me Feel Good To
Complete This Conversation:

Today I Responded The Way My
Spirit Wanted To By:

Speaking Up Daily

Morning Thoughts

Date:

I Feel:

What Is On My Mind This
Morning?

Today I Have Peace In Knowing:

Today I Will Have The Courage To
Say:

I Am Declaring:

Evening Thoughts

How Did I Speak Up For Myself
Today?

I Feel Good Now That I:

Today I Asked:

Today I No Longer Feared:

Based On My Response To The
Previous Prompt, The Result Was:

Today It Made Me Feel Good To
Complete This Conversation:

I Let Go Of The Fear:

Today I Responded The Way My
Spirit Wanted To By:

Today I Set The Boundary:

There Is Power In My Voice.

Speaking Up Daily
Morning Thoughts

Date: I Feel:

What Is On My Mind This   Today I Have Peace In Knowing:
Morning?

Today I Will Have The Courage To   I Am Declaring:
Say:

Evening Thoughts

How Did I Speak Up For Myself   I Feel Good Now That I:
Today?

Today I Asked: Today I No Longer Feared:

Based On My Response To The   Today It Made Me Feel Good To
Previous Prompt, The Result Was: Complete This Conversation:

I Let Go Of The Fear: Today I Responded The Way My
                                                    Spirit Wanted To By:

Today I Set The Boundary:

Speaking Up Daily

Morning Thoughts

Date:

What Is On My Mind This
Morning?

Today I Will Have The Courage To
Say:

I Feel:

Today I Have Peace In Knowing:

I Am Declaring:

Evening Thoughts

How Did I Speak Up For Myself
Today?

Today I Asked:

Based On My Response To The
Previous Prompt, The Result Was:

I Let Go Of The Fear:

Today I Set The Boundary:

I Feel Good Now That I:

Today I No Longer Feared:

Today It Made Me Feel Good To
Complete This Conversation:

Today I Responded The Way My
Spirit Wanted To By:

I Am Courageous.

Speaking Up Daily

Morning Thoughts

Date:

I Feel:

What Is On My Mind This Morning?

Today I Have Peace In Knowing:

Today I Will Have The Courage To Say:

I Am Declaring:

Evening Thoughts

How Did I Speak Up For Myself Today?

I Feel Good Now That I:

Today I Asked:

Today I No Longer Feared:

Based On My Response To The Previous Prompt, The Result Was:

Today It Made Me Feel Good To Complete This Conversation:

I Let Go Of The Fear:

Today I Responded The Way My Spirit Wanted To By:

Today I Set The Boundary:

Speaking Up Daily

Morning Thoughts

Date:

I Feel:

What Is On My Mind This Morning?

Today I Have Peace In Knowing:

Today I Will Have The Courage To Say:

I Am Declaring:

Evening Thoughts

How Did I Speak Up For Myself Today?

I Feel Good Now That I:

Today I Asked:

Today I No Longer Feared:

Based On My Response To The Previous Prompt, The Result Was:

Today It Made Me Feel Good To Complete This Conversation:

I Let Go Of The Fear:

Today I Responded The Way My Spirit Wanted To By:

Today I Set The Boundary:

My Words Are Powerful.

My Thoughts Out Loud

Speaking Up Daily

Morning Thoughts

Date:

What Is On My Mind This
Morning?

Today I Will Have The Courage To
Say:

I Feel:

Today I Have Peace In Knowing:

I Am Declaring:

Evening Thoughts

How Did I Speak Up For Myself
Today?

Today I Asked:

Based On My Response To The
Previous Prompt, The Result Was:

I Let Go Of The Fear:

Today I Set The Boundary:

I Feel Good Now That I:

Today I No Longer Feared:

Today It Made Me Feel Good To
Complete This Conversation:

Today I Responded The Way My
Spirit Wanted To By:

Speaking Up Daily

Morning Thoughts

Date:

I Feel:

What Is On My Mind This
Morning?

Today I Have Peace In Knowing:

Today I Will Have The Courage To
Say:

I Am Declaring:

Evening Thoughts

How Did I Speak Up For Myself
Today?

I Feel Good Now That I:

Today I Asked:

Today I No Longer Feared:

Based On My Response To The
Previous Prompt, The Result Was:

Today It Made Me Feel Good To
Complete This Conversation:

I Let Go Of The Fear:

Today I Responded The Way My
Spirit Wanted To By:

Today I Set The Boundary:

I May Be
Scared But
Once Those
Words Come
Out I Feel
Peace.

No. That
Is A
Complete
Sentence.

Speaking Up Daily

Morning Thoughts

Date:

What Is On My Mind This
Morning?

Today I Will Have The Courage To
Say:

I Feel:

Today I Have Peace In Knowing:

I Am Declaring:

Evening Thoughts

How Did I Speak Up For Myself
Today?

Today I Asked:

Based On My Response To The
Previous Prompt, The Result Was:

I Let Go Of The Fear:

Today I Set The Boundary:

I Feel Good Now That I:

Today I No Longer Feared:

Today It Made Me Feel Good To
Complete This Conversation:

Today I Responded The Way My
Spirit Wanted To By:

Speaking Up Daily

Morning Thoughts

Date:

What Is On My Mind This Morning?

Today I Will Have The Courage To Say:

I Feel:

Today I Have Peace In Knowing:

I Am Declaring:

Evening Thoughts

How Did I Speak Up For Myself Today?

Today I Asked:

Based On My Response To The Previous Prompt, The Result Was:

I Let Go Of The Fear:

Today I Set The Boundary:

I Feel Good Now That I:

Today I No Longer Feared:

Today It Made Me Feel Good To Complete This Conversation:

Today I Responded The Way My Spirit Wanted To By:

It Is Time

To Speak

A Volume

Louder.

My Thoughts Out Loud

Speaking Up Daily

Morning Thoughts

Date:

I Feel:

What Is On My Mind This
Morning?

Today I Have Peace In Knowing:

Today I Will Have The Courage To
Say:

I Am Declaring:

Evening Thoughts

How Did I Speak Up For Myself
Today?

I Feel Good Now That I:

Today I Asked:

Today I No Longer Feared:

Based On My Response To The
Previous Prompt, The Result Was:

Today It Made Me Feel Good To
Complete This Conversation:

I Let Go Of The Fear:

Today I Responded The Way My
Spirit Wanted To By:

Today I Set The Boundary:

Speaking Up Daily

Morning Thoughts

Date: I Feel:

What Is On My Mind This   Today I Have Peace In Knowing:
Morning?

Today I Will Have The Courage To   I Am Declaring:
Say:

Evening Thoughts

How Did I Speak Up For Myself   I Feel Good Now That I:
Today?

Today I Asked: Today I No Longer Feared:

Based On My Response To The   Today It Made Me Feel Good To
Previous Prompt, The Result Was: Complete This Conversation:

I Let Go Of The Fear: Today I Responded The Way My
                                 Spirit Wanted To By:

Today I Set The Boundary:

A List Of The People Who Listen To Me When I Speak....

Speaking Up Daily

Morning Thoughts

Date: I Feel:

What Is On My Mind This   Today I Have Peace In Knowing:
Morning?

Today I Will Have The Courage To   I Am Declaring:
Say:

Evening Thoughts

How Did I Speak Up For Myself   I Feel Good Now That I:
Today?

Today I Asked: Today I No Longer Feared:

Based On My Response To The   Today It Made Me Feel Good To
Previous Prompt, The Result Was: Complete This Conversation:

I Let Go Of The Fear: Today I Responded The Way My
                                    Spirit Wanted To By:

Today I Set The Boundary:

Speaking Up Daily

Morning Thoughts

Date: I Feel:

What Is On My Mind This   Today I Have Peace In Knowing:
Morning?

Today I Will Have The Courage To   I Am Declaring:
Say:

Evening Thoughts

How Did I Speak Up For Myself   I Feel Good Now That I:
Today?

Today I Asked: Today I No Longer Feared:

Based On My Response To The   Today It Made Me Feel Good To
Previous Prompt, The Result Was: Complete This Conversation:

I Let Go Of The Fear: Today I Responded The Way My
                                            Spirit Wanted To By:

Today I Set The Boundary:

I Will No Longer Be Silent About The Things That Matter.

Confrontation Does Not Always Have To Have A Negative Outcome.

Speaking Up Daily

Morning Thoughts

Date:

I Feel:

What Is On My Mind This Morning?

Today I Have Peace In Knowing:

Today I Will Have The Courage To Say:

I Am Declaring:

Evening Thoughts

How Did I Speak Up For Myself Today?

I Feel Good Now That I:

Today I Asked:

Today I No Longer Feared:

Based On My Response To The Previous Prompt, The Result Was:

Today It Made Me Feel Good To Complete This Conversation:

I Let Go Of The Fear:

Today I Responded The Way My Spirit Wanted To By:

Today I Set The Boundary:

I Don't Want People To Like Me Because Of The Things I Don't Say. I Want People To Like Me Because Of My Truth That I Am Able To Express.

Speaking Up Daily

Morning Thoughts

Date: I Feel:

What Is On My Mind This   Today I Have Peace In Knowing:
Morning?

Today I Will Have The Courage To   I Am Declaring:
Say:

Evening Thoughts

How Did I Speak Up For Myself   I Feel Good Now That I:
Today?

Today I Asked: Today I No Longer Feared:

Based On My Response To The   Today It Made Me Feel Good To
Previous Prompt, The Result Was: Complete This Conversation:

I Let Go Of The Fear: Today I Responded The Way My
                                 Spirit Wanted To By:

Today I Set The Boundary:

Speaking Up Daily

Morning Thoughts

Date:

What Is On My Mind This Morning?

Today I Will Have The Courage To Say:

I Feel:

Today I Have Peace In Knowing:

I Am Declaring:

Evening Thoughts

How Did I Speak Up For Myself Today?

Today I Asked:

Based On My Response To The Previous Prompt, The Result Was:

I Let Go Of The Fear:

Today I Set The Boundary:

I Feel Good Now That I:

Today I No Longer Feared:

Today It Made Me Feel Good To Complete This Conversation:

Today I Responded The Way My Spirit Wanted To By:

How Do I Feel When People Interrupt Me When I Am Speaking?

Speaking Up Daily

Morning Thoughts

Date:

I Feel:

What Is On My Mind This
Morning?

Today I Have Peace In Knowing:

Today I Will Have The Courage To
Say:

I Am Declaring:

Evening Thoughts

How Did I Speak Up For Myself
Today?

I Feel Good Now That I:

Today I Asked:

Today I No Longer Feared:

Based On My Response To The
Previous Prompt, The Result Was:

Today It Made Me Feel Good To
Complete This Conversation:

I Let Go Of The Fear:

Today I Responded The Way My
Spirit Wanted To By:

Today I Set The Boundary:

Speaking Up Daily

Morning Thoughts

Date:

I Feel:

What Is On My Mind This
Morning?

Today I Have Peace In Knowing:

Today I Will Have The Courage To
Say:

I Am Declaring:

Evening Thoughts

How Did I Speak Up For Myself
Today?

I Feel Good Now That I:

Today I Asked:

Today I No Longer Feared:

Based On My Response To The
Previous Prompt, The Result Was:

Today It Made Me Feel Good To
Complete This Conversation:

I Let Go Of The Fear:

Today I Responded The Way My
Spirit Wanted To By:

Today I Set The Boundary:

I Will No Longer Just Accept Anything.

Speaking Up Daily

Morning Thoughts

Date:

What Is On My Mind This Morning?

Today I Will Have The Courage To Say:

I Feel:

Today I Have Peace In Knowing:

I Am Declaring:

Evening Thoughts

How Did I Speak Up For Myself Today?

Today I Asked:

Based On My Response To The Previous Prompt, The Result Was:

I Let Go Of The Fear:

Today I Set The Boundary:

I Feel Good Now That I:

Today I No Longer Feared:

Today It Made Me Feel Good To Complete This Conversation:

Today I Responded The Way My Spirit Wanted To By:

Speaking Up Daily

Morning Thoughts

Date:

I Feel:

What Is On My Mind This Morning?

Today I Have Peace In Knowing:

Today I Will Have The Courage To Say:

I Am Declaring:

Evening Thoughts

How Did I Speak Up For Myself Today?

I Feel Good Now That I:

Today I Asked:

Today I No Longer Feared:

Based On My Response To The Previous Prompt, The Result Was:

Today It Made Me Feel Good To Complete This Conversation:

I Let Go Of The Fear:

Today I Responded The Way My Spirit Wanted To By:

Today I Set The Boundary:

Speaking Up Daily

Morning Thoughts

Date:

I Feel:

What Is On My Mind This Morning?

Today I Have Peace In Knowing:

Today I Will Have The Courage To Say:

I Am Declaring:

Evening Thoughts

How Did I Speak Up For Myself Today?

I Feel Good Now That I:

Today I Asked:

Today I No Longer Feared:

Based On My Response To The Previous Prompt, The Result Was:

Today It Made Me Feel Good To Complete This Conversation:

I Let Go Of The Fear:

Today I Responded The Way My Spirit Wanted To By:

Today I Set The Boundary:

They Love Me Because I Love Me.

My Thoughts Out Loud

Speaking Up Daily

Morning Thoughts

Date:

What Is On My Mind This Morning?

Today I Will Have The Courage To Say:

I Feel:

Today I Have Peace In Knowing:

I Am Declaring:

Evening Thoughts

How Did I Speak Up For Myself Today?

Today I Asked:

Based On My Response To The Previous Prompt, The Result Was:

I Let Go Of The Fear:

Today I Set The Boundary:

I Feel Good Now That I:

Today I No Longer Feared:

Today It Made Me Feel Good To Complete This Conversation:

Today I Responded The Way My Spirit Wanted To By:

I Will No Longer Ignore My Feelings Just To Avoid Conflict.

My Voice Matters Just As Much As Theirs.

Speaking Up Daily

Morning Thoughts

Date:

I Feel:

What Is On My Mind This Morning?

Today I Have Peace In Knowing:

Today I Will Have The Courage To Say:

I Am Declaring:

Evening Thoughts

How Did I Speak Up For Myself Today?

I Feel Good Now That I:

Today I Asked:

Today I No Longer Feared:

Based On My Response To The Previous Prompt, The Result Was:

Today It Made Me Feel Good To Complete This Conversation:

I Let Go Of The Fear:

Today I Responded The Way My Spirit Wanted To By:

Today I Set The Boundary:

Speaking Up Daily

Morning Thoughts

Date:

I Feel:

What Is On My Mind This Morning?

Today I Have Peace In Knowing:

Today I Will Have The Courage To Say:

I Am Declaring:

Evening Thoughts

How Did I Speak Up For Myself Today?

I Feel Good Now That I:

Today I Asked:

Today I No Longer Feared:

Based On My Response To The Previous Prompt, The Result Was:

Today It Made Me Feel Good To Complete This Conversation:

I Let Go Of The Fear:

Today I Responded The Way My Spirit Wanted To By:

Today I Set The Boundary:

My Thoughts Out Loud

Speaking Up Daily

Morning Thoughts

Date:

I Feel:

What Is On My Mind This
Morning?

Today I Have Peace In Knowing:

Today I Will Have The Courage To
Say:

I Am Declaring:

Evening Thoughts

How Did I Speak Up For Myself
Today?

I Feel Good Now That I:

Today I Asked:

Today I No Longer Feared:

Based On My Response To The
Previous Prompt, The Result Was:

Today It Made Me Feel Good To
Complete This Conversation:

I Let Go Of The Fear:

Today I Responded The Way My
Spirit Wanted To By:

Today I Set The Boundary:

Speaking Up Daily

Morning Thoughts

Date: I Feel:

What Is On My Mind This   Today I Have Peace In Knowing:
Morning?

Today I Will Have The Courage To   I Am Declaring:
Say:

Evening Thoughts

How Did I Speak Up For Myself   I Feel Good Now That I:
Today?

Today I Asked: Today I No Longer Feared:

Based On My Response To The   Today It Made Me Feel Good To
Previous Prompt, The Result Was: Complete This Conversation:

I Let Go Of The Fear: Today I Responded The Way My
                                          Spirit Wanted To By:

Today I Set The Boundary:

I Am Learning....

Speaking Up Daily

Morning Thoughts

Date: I Feel:

What Is On My Mind This   Today I Have Peace In Knowing:
Morning?

Today I Will Have The Courage To   I Am Declaring:
Say:

Evening Thoughts

How Did I Speak Up For Myself   I Feel Good Now That I:
Today?

Today I Asked: Today I No Longer Feared:

Based On My Response To The   Today It Made Me Feel Good To
Previous Prompt, The Result Was: Complete This Conversation:

I Let Go Of The Fear: Today I Responded The Way My
                                        Spirit Wanted To By:

Today I Set The Boundary:

Speaking Up Daily

Morning Thoughts

Date:

What Is On My Mind This
Morning?

Today I Will Have The Courage To
Say:

I Feel:

Today I Have Peace In Knowing:

I Am Declaring:

Evening Thoughts

How Did I Speak Up For Myself
Today?

Today I Asked:

Based On My Response To The
Previous Prompt, The Result Was:

I Let Go Of The Fear:

Today I Set The Boundary:

I Feel Good Now That I:

Today I No Longer Feared:

Today It Made Me Feel Good To
Complete This Conversation:

Today I Responded The Way My
Spirit Wanted To By:

I Made A Difference By Speaking Up.

I Will No Longer Be Overlooked.

Speaking Up Daily

Morning Thoughts

Date: I Feel:

What Is On My Mind This   Today I Have Peace In Knowing:
Morning?

Today I Will Have The Courage To   I Am Declaring:
Say:

Evening Thoughts

How Did I Speak Up For Myself   I Feel Good Now That I:
Today?

Today I Asked: Today I No Longer Feared:

Based On My Response To The   Today It Made Me Feel Good To
Previous Prompt, The Result Was: Complete This Conversation:

I Let Go Of The Fear: Today I Responded The Way My
                                               Spirit Wanted To By:

Today I Set The Boundary:

Things I Will No Longer Stay Silent About....

My Thoughts Out Loud

Speaking Up Daily

Morning Thoughts

Date: I Feel:

What Is On My Mind This   Today I Have Peace In Knowing:
Morning?

Today I Will Have The Courage To   I Am Declaring:
Say:

Evening Thoughts

How Did I Speak Up For Myself   I Feel Good Now That I:
Today?

Today I Asked: Today I No Longer Feared:

Based On My Response To The   Today It Made Me Feel Good To
Previous Prompt, The Result Was: Complete This Conversation:

I Let Go Of The Fear: Today I Responded The Way My
                                   Spirit Wanted To By:

Today I Set The Boundary:

Speaking Up Daily

Morning Thoughts

Date:

I Feel:

What Is On My Mind This Morning?

Today I Have Peace In Knowing:

Today I Will Have The Courage To Say:

I Am Declaring:

Evening Thoughts

How Did I Speak Up For Myself Today?

I Feel Good Now That I:

Today I Asked:

Today I No Longer Feared:

Based On My Response To The Previous Prompt, The Result Was:

Today It Made Me Feel Good To Complete This Conversation:

I Let Go Of The Fear:

Today I Responded The Way My Spirit Wanted To By:

Today I Set The Boundary:

Speaking Up Daily

Morning Thoughts

Date:

I Feel:

What Is On My Mind This Morning?

Today I Have Peace In Knowing:

Today I Will Have The Courage To Say:

I Am Declaring:

Evening Thoughts

How Did I Speak Up For Myself Today?

I Feel Good Now That I:

Today I Asked:

Today I No Longer Feared:

Based On My Response To The Previous Prompt, The Result Was:

Today It Made Me Feel Good To Complete This Conversation:

I Let Go Of The Fear:

Today I Responded The Way My Spirit Wanted To By:

Today I Set The Boundary:

It Is Through Communication I Can Feel At Peace.

I Am At Peace
Losing What
Wants To Leave
Because I Have
Stated My
Standards.

Speaking Up Daily

Morning Thoughts

Date:

I Feel:

What Is On My Mind This Morning?

Today I Have Peace In Knowing:

Today I Will Have The Courage To Say:

I Am Declaring:

Evening Thoughts

How Did I Speak Up For Myself Today?

I Feel Good Now That I:

Today I Asked:

Today I No Longer Feared:

Based On My Response To The Previous Prompt, The Result Was:

Today It Made Me Feel Good To Complete This Conversation:

I Let Go Of The Fear:

Today I Responded The Way My Spirit Wanted To By:

Today I Set The Boundary:

The Same Way I Am Able To Attend To The Needs Of Others Is The Same Way I Am Able To Attend To My Needs.

My Thoughts Out Loud

Speaking Up Daily

Morning Thoughts

Date:

I Feel:

What Is On My Mind This Morning?

Today I Have Peace In Knowing:

Today I Will Have The Courage To Say:

I Am Declaring:

Evening Thoughts

How Did I Speak Up For Myself Today?

I Feel Good Now That I:

Today I Asked:

Today I No Longer Feared:

Based On My Response To The Previous Prompt, The Result Was:

Today It Made Me Feel Good To Complete This Conversation:

I Let Go Of The Fear:

Today I Responded The Way My Spirit Wanted To By:

Today I Set The Boundary:

Speaking Up Daily

Morning Thoughts

Date:

I Feel:

What Is On My Mind This
Morning?

Today I Have Peace In Knowing:

Today I Will Have The Courage To
Say:

I Am Declaring:

Evening Thoughts

How Did I Speak Up For Myself
Today?

I Feel Good Now That I:

Today I Asked:

Today I No Longer Feared:

Based On My Response To The
Previous Prompt, The Result Was:

Today It Made Me Feel Good To
Complete This Conversation:

I Let Go Of The Fear:

Today I Responded The Way My
Spirit Wanted To By:

Today I Set The Boundary:

Speaking Up Daily

Morning Thoughts

Date:

I Feel:

What Is On My Mind This
Morning?

Today I Have Peace In Knowing:

Today I Will Have The Courage To
Say:

I Am Declaring:

Evening Thoughts

How Did I Speak Up For Myself
Today?

I Feel Good Now That I:

Today I Asked:

Today I No Longer Feared:

Based On My Response To The
Previous Prompt, The Result Was:

Today It Made Me Feel Good To
Complete This Conversation:

I Let Go Of The Fear:

Today I Responded The Way My
Spirit Wanted To By:

Today I Set The Boundary:

132

My Thoughts Out Loud

I Wanted Changes So I Spoke Up.

Speaking Up Daily

Morning Thoughts

Date: I Feel:

What Is On My Mind This   Today I Have Peace In Knowing:
Morning?

Today I Will Have The Courage To   I Am Declaring:
Say:

Evening Thoughts

How Did I Speak Up For Myself   I Feel Good Now That I:
Today?

Today I Asked: Today I No Longer Feared:

Based On My Response To The   Today It Made Me Feel Good To
Previous Prompt, The Result Was: Complete This Conversation:

I Let Go Of The Fear: Today I Responded The Way My
                                         Spirit Wanted To By:

Today I Set The Boundary:

Speaking Up Daily

Morning Thoughts

Date:

What Is On My Mind This
Morning?

Today I Will Have The Courage To
Say:

I Feel:

Today I Have Peace In Knowing:

I Am Declaring:

Evening Thoughts

How Did I Speak Up For Myself
Today?

Today I Asked:

Based On My Response To The
Previous Prompt, The Result Was:

I Let Go Of The Fear:

Today I Set The Boundary:

I Feel Good Now That I:

Today I No Longer Feared:

Today It Made Me Feel Good To
Complete This Conversation:

Today I Responded The Way My
Spirit Wanted To By:

Speaking Up Daily

Morning Thoughts

Date: I Feel:

What Is On My Mind This   Today I Have Peace In Knowing:
Morning?

Today I Will Have The Courage To   I Am Declaring:
Say:

Evening Thoughts

How Did I Speak Up For Myself   I Feel Good Now That I:
Today?

Today I Asked: Today I No Longer Feared:

Based On My Response To The   Today It Made Me Feel Good To
Previous Prompt, The Result Was: Complete This Conversation:

I Let Go Of The Fear: Today I Responded The Way My
                                     Spirit Wanted To By:

Today I Set The Boundary:

I Got It Because I Had The Courage To Ask For It.

My Thoughts Out Loud

Speaking Up Daily

Morning Thoughts

Date:

What Is On My Mind This Morning?

Today I Will Have The Courage To Say:

I Feel:

Today I Have Peace In Knowing:

I Am Declaring:

Evening Thoughts

How Did I Speak Up For Myself Today?

Today I Asked:

Based On My Response To The Previous Prompt, The Result Was:

I Let Go Of The Fear:

Today I Set The Boundary:

I Feel Good Now That I:

Today I No Longer Feared:

Today It Made Me Feel Good To Complete This Conversation:

Today I Responded The Way My Spirit Wanted To By:

Speaking Up Daily

Morning Thoughts

Date:

I Feel:

What Is On My Mind This Morning?

Today I Have Peace In Knowing:

Today I Will Have The Courage To Say:

I Am Declaring:

Evening Thoughts

How Did I Speak Up For Myself Today?

I Feel Good Now That I:

Today I Asked:

Today I No Longer Feared:

Based On My Response To The Previous Prompt, The Result Was:

Today It Made Me Feel Good To Complete This Conversation:

I Let Go Of The Fear:

Today I Responded The Way My Spirit Wanted To By:

Today I Set The Boundary:

I Will Always
Speak
Up When
Boundaries
Are Crossed.

Speaking Up Daily

Morning Thoughts

Date:

I Feel:

What Is On My Mind This Morning?

Today I Have Peace In Knowing:

Today I Will Have The Courage To Say:

I Am Declaring:

Evening Thoughts

How Did I Speak Up For Myself Today?

I Feel Good Now That I:

Today I Asked:

Today I No Longer Feared:

Based On My Response To The Previous Prompt, The Result Was:

Today It Made Me Feel Good To Complete This Conversation:

I Let Go Of The Fear:

Today I Responded The Way My Spirit Wanted To By:

Today I Set The Boundary:

Speaking Up Daily

Morning Thoughts

Date:

I Feel:

What Is On My Mind This Morning?

Today I Have Peace In Knowing:

Today I Will Have The Courage To Say:

I Am Declaring:

Evening Thoughts

How Did I Speak Up For Myself Today?

I Feel Good Now That I:

Today I Asked:

Today I No Longer Feared:

Based On My Response To The Previous Prompt, The Result Was:

Today It Made Me Feel Good To Complete This Conversation:

I Let Go Of The Fear:

Today I Responded The Way My Spirit Wanted To By:

Today I Set The Boundary:

Speaking Up Daily

Morning Thoughts

Date:

I Feel:

What Is On My Mind This Morning?

Today I Have Peace In Knowing:

Today I Will Have The Courage To Say:

I Am Declaring:

Evening Thoughts

How Did I Speak Up For Myself Today?

I Feel Good Now That I:

Today I Asked:

Today I No Longer Feared:

Based On My Response To The Previous Prompt, The Result Was:

Today It Made Me Feel Good To Complete This Conversation:

I Let Go Of The Fear:

Today I Responded The Way My Spirit Wanted To By:

Today I Set The Boundary:

Now When I Speak....

Speaking Up Daily

Morning Thoughts

Date:

I Feel:

What Is On My Mind This Morning?

Today I Have Peace In Knowing:

Today I Will Have The Courage To Say:

I Am Declaring:

Evening Thoughts

How Did I Speak Up For Myself Today?

I Feel Good Now That I:

Today I Asked:

Today I No Longer Feared:

Based On My Response To The Previous Prompt, The Result Was:

Today It Made Me Feel Good To Complete This Conversation:

I Let Go Of The Fear:

Today I Responded The Way My Spirit Wanted To By:

Today I Set The Boundary:

Speaking Up Daily

Morning Thoughts

Date:

I Feel:

What Is On My Mind This Morning?

Today I Have Peace In Knowing:

Today I Will Have The Courage To Say:

I Am Declaring:

Evening Thoughts

How Did I Speak Up For Myself Today?

I Feel Good Now That I:

Today I Asked:

Today I No Longer Feared:

Based On My Response To The Previous Prompt, The Result Was:

Today It Made Me Feel Good To Complete This Conversation:

I Let Go Of The Fear:

Today I Responded The Way My Spirit Wanted To By:

Today I Set The Boundary:

Speaking Up Daily

Morning Thoughts

Date:

I Feel:

What Is On My Mind This
Morning?

Today I Have Peace In Knowing:

Today I Will Have The Courage To
Say:

I Am Declaring:

Evening Thoughts

How Did I Speak Up For Myself
Today?

I Feel Good Now That I:

Today I Asked:

Today I No Longer Feared:

Based On My Response To The
Previous Prompt, The Result Was:

Today It Made Me Feel Good To
Complete This Conversation:

I Let Go Of The Fear:

Today I Responded The Way My
Spirit Wanted To By:

Today I Set The Boundary:

I Mean Every Word I Say.

My Thoughts Out Loud

Speaking Up Daily

Morning Thoughts

Date:

I Feel:

What Is On My Mind This Morning?

Today I Have Peace In Knowing:

Today I Will Have The Courage To Say:

I Am Declaring:

Evening Thoughts

How Did I Speak Up For Myself Today?

I Feel Good Now That I:

Today I Asked:

Today I No Longer Feared:

Based On My Response To The Previous Prompt, The Result Was:

Today It Made Me Feel Good To Complete This Conversation:

I Let Go Of The Fear:

Today I Responded The Way My Spirit Wanted To By:

Today I Set The Boundary:

Speaking Up Daily

Morning Thoughts

Date:

I Feel:

What Is On My Mind This Morning?

Today I Have Peace In Knowing:

Today I Will Have The Courage To Say:

I Am Declaring:

Evening Thoughts

How Did I Speak Up For Myself Today?

I Feel Good Now That I:

Today I Asked:

Today I No Longer Feared:

Based On My Response To The Previous Prompt, The Result Was:

Today It Made Me Feel Good To Complete This Conversation:

I Let Go Of The Fear:

Today I Responded The Way My Spirit Wanted To By:

Today I Set The Boundary:

Speaking Up Daily
Morning Thoughts

Date:

What Is On My Mind This
Morning?

Today I Will Have The Courage To
Say:

I Feel:

Today I Have Peace In Knowing:

I Am Declaring:

Evening Thoughts

How Did I Speak Up For Myself
Today?

Today I Asked:

Based On My Response To The
Previous Prompt, The Result Was:

I Let Go Of The Fear:

Today I Set The Boundary:

I Feel Good Now That I:

Today I No Longer Feared:

Today It Made Me Feel Good To
Complete This Conversation:

Today I Responded The Way My
Spirit Wanted To By:

Speaking Up
For Myself
Is My Way
Of Showing
Love Towards
Myself.

My
Words
Are
Golden.

My Thoughts Out Loud

Speaking Up Daily
Morning Thoughts

Date: I Feel:

What Is On My Mind This   Today I Have Peace In Knowing:
Morning?

Today I Will Have The Courage To   I Am Declaring:
Say:

Evening Thoughts

How Did I Speak Up For Myself   I Feel Good Now That I:
Today?

Today I Asked: Today I No Longer Feared:

Based On My Response To The   Today It Made Me Feel Good To
Previous Prompt, The Result Was: Complete This Conversation:

I Let Go Of The Fear: Today I Responded The Way My
                                                Spirit Wanted To By:

Today I Set The Boundary:

Speaking Up Daily

Morning Thoughts

Date:

I Feel:

What Is On My Mind This Morning?

Today I Have Peace In Knowing:

Today I Will Have The Courage To Say:

I Am Declaring:

Evening Thoughts

How Did I Speak Up For Myself Today?

I Feel Good Now That I:

Today I Asked:

Today I No Longer Feared:

Based On My Response To The Previous Prompt, The Result Was:

Today It Made Me Feel Good To Complete This Conversation:

I Let Go Of The Fear:

Today I Responded The Way My Spirit Wanted To By:

Today I Set The Boundary:

The Way I Speak About About Myself Matters.

Speaking Up Daily

Morning Thoughts

Date:

I Feel:

What Is On My Mind This
Morning?

Today I Have Peace In Knowing:

Today I Will Have The Courage To
Say:

I Am Declaring:

Evening Thoughts

How Did I Speak Up For Myself
Today?

I Feel Good Now That I:

Today I Asked:

Today I No Longer Feared:

Based On My Response To The
Previous Prompt, The Result Was:

Today It Made Me Feel Good To
Complete This Conversation:

I Let Go Of The Fear:

Today I Responded The Way My
Spirit Wanted To By:

Today I Set The Boundary:

I Speak The Truth.

I Will Not Be Confined To The Thoughts In My Head.

Speaking Up Daily

Morning Thoughts

Date: I Feel:

What Is On My Mind This   Today I Have Peace In Knowing:
Morning?

Today I Will Have The Courage To   I Am Declaring:
Say:

Evening Thoughts

How Did I Speak Up For Myself   I Feel Good Now That I:
Today?

Today I Asked: Today I No Longer Feared:

Based On My Response To The   Today It Made Me Feel Good To
Previous Prompt, The Result Was: Complete This Conversation:

I Let Go Of The Fear: Today I Responded The Way My
                                               Spirit Wanted To By:

Today I Set The Boundary:

Speaking Up Daily

Morning Thoughts

Date: I Feel:

What Is On My Mind This   Today I Have Peace In Knowing:
Morning?

Today I Will Have The Courage To   I Am Declaring:
Say:

Evening Thoughts

How Did I Speak Up For Myself   I Feel Good Now That I:
Today?

Today I Asked: Today I No Longer Feared:

Based On My Response To The   Today It Made Me Feel Good To
Previous Prompt, The Result Was: Complete This Conversation:

I Let Go Of The Fear: Today I Responded The Way My
                                                Spirit Wanted To By:

Today I Set The Boundary:

My Thoughts Out Loud

I Am Fearless.

Speaking Up Daily

Morning Thoughts

Date:

I Feel:

What Is On My Mind This Morning?

Today I Have Peace In Knowing:

Today I Will Have The Courage To Say:

I Am Declaring:

Evening Thoughts

How Did I Speak Up For Myself Today?

I Feel Good Now That I:

Today I Asked:

Today I No Longer Feared:

Based On My Response To The Previous Prompt, The Result Was:

Today It Made Me Feel Good To Complete This Conversation:

I Let Go Of The Fear:

Today I Responded The Way My Spirit Wanted To By:

Today I Set The Boundary:

Speaking Up Daily

Morning Thoughts

Date: I Feel:

What Is On My Mind This   Today I Have Peace In Knowing:
Morning?

Today I Will Have The Courage To   I Am Declaring:
Say:

Evening Thoughts

How Did I Speak Up For Myself   I Feel Good Now That I:
Today?

Today I Asked: Today I No Longer Feared:

Based On My Response To The   Today It Made Me Feel Good To
Previous Prompt, The Result Was: Complete This Conversation:

I Let Go Of The Fear: Today I Responded The Way My
                                 Spirit Wanted To By:

Today I Set The Boundary:

The Only Thing I Will Remain Silent About....

Speaking Up Daily

Morning Thoughts

Date:

I Feel:

What Is On My Mind This Morning?

Today I Have Peace In Knowing:

Today I Will Have The Courage To Say:

I Am Declaring:

Evening Thoughts

How Did I Speak Up For Myself Today?

I Feel Good Now That I:

Today I Asked:

Today I No Longer Feared:

Based On My Response To The Previous Prompt, The Result Was:

Today It Made Me Feel Good To Complete This Conversation:

I Let Go Of The Fear:

Today I Responded The Way My Spirit Wanted To By:

Today I Set The Boundary:

Speaking Up Daily

Morning Thoughts

Date:

I Feel:

What Is On My Mind This Morning?

Today I Have Peace In Knowing:

Today I Will Have The Courage To Say:

I Am Declaring:

Evening Thoughts

How Did I Speak Up For Myself Today?

I Feel Good Now That I:

Today I Asked:

Today I No Longer Feared:

Based On My Response To The Previous Prompt, The Result Was:

Today It Made Me Feel Good To Complete This Conversation:

I Let Go Of The Fear:

Today I Responded The Way My Spirit Wanted To By:

Today I Set The Boundary:

Since Speaking Up For Myself With Family/Friends/Partner/Coworker, I....

Speaking Up Daily

Morning Thoughts

Date:

I Feel:

What Is On My Mind This Morning?

Today I Have Peace In Knowing:

Today I Will Have The Courage To Say:

I Am Declaring:

Evening Thoughts

How Did I Speak Up For Myself Today?

I Feel Good Now That I:

Today I Asked:

Today I No Longer Feared:

Based On My Response To The Previous Prompt, The Result Was:

Today It Made Me Feel Good To Complete This Conversation:

I Let Go Of The Fear:

Today I Responded The Way My Spirit Wanted To By:

Today I Set The Boundary:

Speaking Up Daily

Morning Thoughts

Date: I Feel:

What Is On My Mind This   Today I Have Peace In Knowing:
Morning?

Today I Will Have The Courage To   I Am Declaring:
Say:

Evening Thoughts

How Did I Speak Up For Myself   I Feel Good Now That I:
Today?

Today I Asked: Today I No Longer Feared:

Based On My Response To The   Today It Made Me Feel Good To
Previous Prompt, The Result Was: Complete This Conversation:

I Let Go Of The Fear: Today I Responded The Way My
                                       Spirit Wanted To By:

Today I Set The Boundary:

When I Speak, I Speak From A Place Of Love.

Speaking Up Daily

Morning Thoughts

Date:

I Feel:

What Is On My Mind This Morning?

Today I Have Peace In Knowing:

Today I Will Have The Courage To Say:

I Am Declaring:

Evening Thoughts

How Did I Speak Up For Myself Today?

I Feel Good Now That I:

Today I Asked:

Today I No Longer Feared:

Based On My Response To The Previous Prompt, The Result Was:

Today It Made Me Feel Good To Complete This Conversation:

I Let Go Of The Fear:

Today I Responded The Way My Spirit Wanted To By:

Today I Set The Boundary:

Speaking Up Daily

Morning Thoughts

Date: I Feel:

What Is On My Mind This   Today I Have Peace In Knowing:
Morning?

Today I Will Have The Courage To   I Am Declaring:
Say:

Evening Thoughts

How Did I Speak Up For Myself   I Feel Good Now That I:
Today?

Today I Asked: Today I No Longer Feared:

Based On My Response To The   Today It Made Me Feel Good To
Previous Prompt, The Result Was: Complete This Conversation:

I Let Go Of The Fear: Today I Responded The Way My
                                         Spirit Wanted To By:

Today I Set The Boundary:

My Thoughts Out Loud

Speaking Up Daily

Morning Thoughts

Date:

What Is On My Mind This Morning?

Today I Will Have The Courage To Say:

I Feel:

Today I Have Peace In Knowing:

I Am Declaring:

Evening Thoughts

How Did I Speak Up For Myself Today?

Today I Asked:

Based On My Response To The Previous Prompt, The Result Was:

I Let Go Of The Fear:

Today I Set The Boundary:

I Feel Good Now That I:

Today I No Longer Feared:

Today It Made Me Feel Good To Complete This Conversation:

Today I Responded The Way My Spirit Wanted To By:

Speaking Up Daily

Morning Thoughts

Date:

I Feel:

What Is On My Mind This Morning?

Today I Have Peace In Knowing:

Today I Will Have The Courage To Say:

I Am Declaring:

Evening Thoughts

How Did I Speak Up For Myself Today?

I Feel Good Now That I:

Today I Asked:

Today I No Longer Feared:

Based On My Response To The Previous Prompt, The Result Was:

Today It Made Me Feel Good To Complete This Conversation:

I Let Go Of The Fear:

Today I Responded The Way My Spirit Wanted To By:

Today I Set The Boundary:

I Have A Very Passionate Spirit.

Speaking Up Daily

Morning Thoughts

Date: I Feel:

What Is On My Mind This   Today I Have Peace In Knowing:
Morning?

Today I Will Have The Courage To   I Am Declaring:
Say:

Evening Thoughts

How Did I Speak Up For Myself   I Feel Good Now That I:
Today?

Today I Asked: Today I No Longer Feared:

Based On My Response To The   Today It Made Me Feel Good To
Previous Prompt, The Result Was: Complete This Conversation:

I Let Go Of The Fear: Today I Responded The Way My
                                     Spirit Wanted To By:

Today I Set The Boundary:

Speaking Up Daily

Morning Thoughts

Date: I Feel:

What Is On My Mind This   Today I Have Peace In Knowing:
Morning?

Today I Will Have The Courage To   I Am Declaring:
Say:

Evening Thoughts

How Did I Speak Up For Myself   I Feel Good Now That I:
Today?

Today I Asked: Today I No Longer Feared:

Based On My Response To The   Today It Made Me Feel Good To
Previous Prompt, The Result Was: Complete This Conversation:

I Let Go Of The Fear: Today I Responded The Way My
                                        Spirit Wanted To By:

Today I Set The Boundary:

Speaking Up Daily

Morning Thoughts

Date:

I Feel:

What Is On My Mind This Morning?

Today I Have Peace In Knowing:

Today I Will Have The Courage To Say:

I Am Declaring:

Evening Thoughts

How Did I Speak Up For Myself Today?

I Feel Good Now That I:

Today I Asked:

Today I No Longer Feared:

Based On My Response To The Previous Prompt, The Result Was:

Today It Made Me Feel Good To Complete This Conversation:

I Let Go Of The Fear:

Today I Responded The Way My Spirit Wanted To By:

Today I Set The Boundary:

My Thoughts Out Loud

When I Speak, I Make My Point.

Speaking Up Daily

Morning Thoughts

Date:

What Is On My Mind This
Morning?

Today I Will Have The Courage To
Say:

I Feel:

Today I Have Peace In Knowing:

I Am Declaring:

Evening Thoughts

How Did I Speak Up For Myself
Today?

Today I Asked:

Based On My Response To The
Previous Prompt, The Result Was:

I Let Go Of The Fear:

Today I Set The Boundary:

I Feel Good Now That I:

Today I No Longer Feared:

Today It Made Me Feel Good To
Complete This Conversation:

Today I Responded The Way My
Spirit Wanted To By:

Speaking Up Daily

Morning Thoughts

Date: I Feel:

What Is On My Mind This   Today I Have Peace In Knowing:
Morning?

Today I Will Have The Courage To   I Am Declaring:
Say:

Evening Thoughts

How Did I Speak Up For Myself   I Feel Good Now That I:
Today?

Today I Asked: Today I No Longer Feared:

Based On My Response To The   Today It Made Me Feel Good To
Previous Prompt, The Result Was: Complete This Conversation:

I Let Go Of The Fear: Today I Responded The Way My
                                         Spirit Wanted To By:

Today I Set The Boundary:

Speaking Up Daily

Morning Thoughts

Date:

I Feel:

What Is On My Mind This Morning?

Today I Have Peace In Knowing:

Today I Will Have The Courage To Say:

I Am Declaring:

Evening Thoughts

How Did I Speak Up For Myself Today?

I Feel Good Now That I:

Today I Asked:

Today I No Longer Feared:

Based On My Response To The Previous Prompt, The Result Was:

Today It Made Me Feel Good To Complete This Conversation:

I Let Go Of The Fear:

Today I Responded The Way My Spirit Wanted To By:

Today I Set The Boundary:

I Was Able To Heal After I Said....

Speaking Up Daily

Morning Thoughts

Date:

I Feel:

What Is On My Mind This Morning?

Today I Have Peace In Knowing:

Today I Will Have The Courage To Say:

I Am Declaring:

Evening Thoughts

How Did I Speak Up For Myself Today?

I Feel Good Now That I:

Today I Asked:

Today I No Longer Feared:

Based On My Response To The Previous Prompt, The Result Was:

Today It Made Me Feel Good To Complete This Conversation:

I Let Go Of The Fear:

Today I Responded The Way My Spirit Wanted To By:

Today I Set The Boundary:

Speaking Up Daily

Morning Thoughts

Date:

I Feel:

What Is On My Mind This Morning?

Today I Have Peace In Knowing:

Today I Will Have The Courage To Say:

I Am Declaring:

Evening Thoughts

How Did I Speak Up For Myself Today?

I Feel Good Now That I:

Today I Asked:

Today I No Longer Feared:

Based On My Response To The Previous Prompt, The Result Was:

Today It Made Me Feel Good To Complete This Conversation:

I Let Go Of The Fear:

Today I Responded The Way My Spirit Wanted To By:

Today I Set The Boundary:

I Use Very Few Words To Say A Lot.

My Words Create Life.

Speaking Up Daily

Morning Thoughts

Date:

I Feel:

What Is On My Mind This Morning?

Today I Have Peace In Knowing:

Today I Will Have The Courage To Say:

I Am Declaring:

Evening Thoughts

How Did I Speak Up For Myself Today?

I Feel Good Now That I:

Today I Asked:

Today I No Longer Feared:

Based On My Response To The Previous Prompt, The Result Was:

Today It Made Me Feel Good To Complete This Conversation:

I Let Go Of The Fear:

Today I Responded The Way My Spirit Wanted To By:

Today I Set The Boundary:

Speaking Up Daily

Morning Thoughts

Date:

I Feel:

What Is On My Mind This
Morning?

Today I Have Peace In Knowing:

Today I Will Have The Courage To
Say:

I Am Declaring:

Evening Thoughts

How Did I Speak Up For Myself
Today?

I Feel Good Now That I:

Today I Asked:

Today I No Longer Feared:

Based On My Response To The
Previous Prompt, The Result Was:

Today It Made Me Feel Good To
Complete This Conversation:

I Let Go Of The Fear:

Today I Responded The Way My
Spirit Wanted To By:

Today I Set The Boundary:

I Forgive Myself For All Of Those Times I Silenced Myself.

I Would Rather
Feel Good For
Speaking Up For
Myself Then Feel
Bad For Not
Saying Anything.

Speaking Up Daily

Morning Thoughts

Date:

I Feel:

What Is On My Mind This Morning?

Today I Have Peace In Knowing:

Today I Will Have The Courage To Say:

I Am Declaring:

Evening Thoughts

How Did I Speak Up For Myself Today?

I Feel Good Now That I:

Today I Asked:

Today I No Longer Feared:

Based On My Response To The Previous Prompt, The Result Was:

Today It Made Me Feel Good To Complete This Conversation:

I Let Go Of The Fear:

Today I Responded The Way My Spirit Wanted To By:

Today I Set The Boundary:

Speaking Up Daily

Morning Thoughts

Date:

I Feel:

What Is On My Mind This Morning?

Today I Have Peace In Knowing:

Today I Will Have The Courage To Say:

I Am Declaring:

Evening Thoughts

How Did I Speak Up For Myself Today?

I Feel Good Now That I:

Today I Asked:

Today I No Longer Feared:

Based On My Response To The Previous Prompt, The Result Was:

Today It Made Me Feel Good To Complete This Conversation:

I Let Go Of The Fear:

Today I Responded The Way My Spirit Wanted To By:

Today I Set The Boundary:

My Thoughts Out Loud

Speaking Up Daily
Morning Thoughts

Date:

I Feel:

What Is On My Mind This Morning?

Today I Have Peace In Knowing:

Today I Will Have The Courage To Say:

I Am Declaring:

Evening Thoughts

How Did I Speak Up For Myself Today?

I Feel Good Now That I:

Today I Asked:

Today I No Longer Feared:

Based On My Response To The Previous Prompt, The Result Was:

Today It Made Me Feel Good To Complete This Conversation:

I Let Go Of The Fear:

Today I Responded The Way My Spirit Wanted To By:

Today I Set The Boundary:

Speaking Up Daily

Morning Thoughts

Date: I Feel:

What Is On My Mind This   Today I Have Peace In Knowing:
Morning?

Today I Will Have The Courage To   I Am Declaring:
Say:

Evening Thoughts

How Did I Speak Up For Myself   I Feel Good Now That I:
Today?

Today I Asked: Today I No Longer Feared:

Based On My Response To The   Today It Made Me Feel Good To
Previous Prompt, The Result Was: Complete This Conversation:

I Let Go Of The Fear: Today I Responded The Way My
                                     Spirit Wanted To By:

Today I Set The Boundary:

Speaking Up Daily

Morning Thoughts

Date:

I Feel:

What Is On My Mind This Morning?

Today I Have Peace In Knowing:

Today I Will Have The Courage To Say:

I Am Declaring:

Evening Thoughts

How Did I Speak Up For Myself Today?

I Feel Good Now That I:

Today I Asked:

Today I No Longer Feared:

Based On My Response To The Previous Prompt, The Result Was:

Today It Made Me Feel Good To Complete This Conversation:

I Let Go Of The Fear:

Today I Responded The Way My Spirit Wanted To By:

Today I Set The Boundary:

I Am My Own Best Friend.

My Thoughts Out Loud

Speaking Up Daily

Morning Thoughts

Date: I Feel:

What Is On My Mind This   Today I Have Peace In Knowing:
Morning?

Today I Will Have The Courage To   I Am Declaring:
Say:

Evening Thoughts

How Did I Speak Up For Myself   I Feel Good Now That I:
Today?

Today I Asked: Today I No Longer Feared:

Based On My Response To The   Today It Made Me Feel Good To
Previous Prompt, The Result Was: Complete This Conversation:

I Let Go Of The Fear: Today I Responded The Way My
                                         Spirit Wanted To By:

Today I Set The Boundary:

Speaking Up Daily

Morning Thoughts

Date:

What Is On My Mind This
Morning?

Today I Will Have The Courage To
Say:

I Feel:

Today I Have Peace In Knowing:

I Am Declaring:

Evening Thoughts

How Did I Speak Up For Myself
Today?

Today I Asked:

Based On My Response To The
Previous Prompt, The Result Was:

I Let Go Of The Fear:

Today I Set The Boundary:

I Feel Good Now That I:

Today I No Longer Feared:

Today It Made Me Feel Good To
Complete This Conversation:

Today I Responded The Way My
Spirit Wanted To By:

Speaking Up Daily

Morning Thoughts

Date:

I Feel:

What Is On My Mind This Morning?

Today I Have Peace In Knowing:

Today I Will Have The Courage To Say:

I Am Declaring:

Evening Thoughts

How Did I Speak Up For Myself Today?

I Feel Good Now That I:

Today I Asked:

Today I No Longer Feared:

Based On My Response To The Previous Prompt, The Result Was:

Today It Made Me Feel Good To Complete This Conversation:

I Let Go Of The Fear:

Today I Responded The Way My Spirit Wanted To By:

Today I Set The Boundary:

God Has My Back.

It Does Not
Matter What
People Think Of
Me Because I
Choose To Speak
Up For Myself.

Speaking Up Daily

Morning Thoughts

Date:

I Feel:

What Is On My Mind This Morning?

Today I Have Peace In Knowing:

Today I Will Have The Courage To Say:

I Am Declaring:

Evening Thoughts

How Did I Speak Up For Myself Today?

I Feel Good Now That I:

Today I Asked:

Today I No Longer Feared:

Based On My Response To The Previous Prompt, The Result Was:

Today It Made Me Feel Good To Complete This Conversation:

I Let Go Of The Fear:

Today I Responded The Way My Spirit Wanted To By:

Today I Set The Boundary:

Speaking Up Daily

Morning Thoughts

Date:

What Is On My Mind This
Morning?

Today I Will Have The Courage To
Say:

I Feel:

Today I Have Peace In Knowing:

I Am Declaring:

Evening Thoughts

How Did I Speak Up For Myself
Today?

Today I Asked:

Based On My Response To The
Previous Prompt, The Result Was:

I Let Go Of The Fear:

Today I Set The Boundary:

I Feel Good Now That I:

Today I No Longer Feared:

Today It Made Me Feel Good To
Complete This Conversation:

Today I Responded The Way My
Spirit Wanted To By:

Speaking Up Daily

Morning Thoughts

Date:

I Feel:

What Is On My Mind This
Morning?

Today I Have Peace In Knowing:

Today I Will Have The Courage To
Say:

I Am Declaring:

Evening Thoughts

How Did I Speak Up For Myself
Today?

I Feel Good Now That I:

Today I Asked:

Today I No Longer Feared:

Based On My Response To The
Previous Prompt, The Result Was:

Today It Made Me Feel Good To
Complete This Conversation:

I Let Go Of The Fear:

Today I Responded The Way My
Spirit Wanted To By:

Today I Set The Boundary:

I Will Always Speak Up For Myself Even If That Means Standing And Speaking Alone.

My Thoughts Out Loud

Speaking Up Daily

Morning Thoughts

Date:

I Feel:

What Is On My Mind This Morning?

Today I Have Peace In Knowing:

Today I Will Have The Courage To Say:

I Am Declaring:

Evening Thoughts

How Did I Speak Up For Myself Today?

I Feel Good Now That I:

Today I Asked:

Today I No Longer Feared:

Based On My Response To The Previous Prompt, The Result Was:

Today It Made Me Feel Good To Complete This Conversation:

I Let Go Of The Fear:

Today I Responded The Way My Spirit Wanted To By:

Today I Set The Boundary:

Speaking Up Daily
Morning Thoughts

Date:

I Feel:

What Is On My Mind This Morning?

Today I Have Peace In Knowing:

Today I Will Have The Courage To Say:

I Am Declaring:

Evening Thoughts

How Did I Speak Up For Myself Today?

I Feel Good Now That I:

Today I Asked:

Today I No Longer Feared:

Based On My Response To The Previous Prompt, The Result Was:

Today It Made Me Feel Good To Complete This Conversation:

I Let Go Of The Fear:

Today I Responded The Way My Spirit Wanted To By:

Today I Set The Boundary:

Speaking Up Daily

Morning Thoughts

Date:

What Is On My Mind This
Morning?

Today I Will Have The Courage To
Say:

I Feel:

Today I Have Peace In Knowing:

I Am Declaring:

Evening Thoughts

How Did I Speak Up For Myself
Today?

Today I Asked:

Based On My Response To The
Previous Prompt, The Result Was:

I Let Go Of The Fear:

Today I Set The Boundary:

I Feel Good Now That I:

Today I No Longer Feared:

Today It Made Me Feel Good To
Complete This Conversation:

Today I Responded The Way My
Spirit Wanted To By:

The More I Speak Up For Myself, The More My Confidence Grows.

Speaking Up Daily

Morning Thoughts

Date:

I Feel:

What Is On My Mind This Morning?

Today I Have Peace In Knowing:

Today I Will Have The Courage To Say:

I Am Declaring:

Evening Thoughts

How Did I Speak Up For Myself Today?

I Feel Good Now That I:

Today I Asked:

Today I No Longer Feared:

Based On My Response To The Previous Prompt, The Result Was:

Today It Made Me Feel Good To Complete This Conversation:

I Let Go Of The Fear:

Today I Responded The Way My Spirit Wanted To By:

Today I Set The Boundary:

Speaking Up Daily

Morning Thoughts

Date: I Feel:

What Is On My Mind This   Today I Have Peace In Knowing:
Morning?

Today I Will Have The Courage To   I Am Declaring:
Say:

Evening Thoughts

How Did I Speak Up For Myself   I Feel Good Now That I:
Today?

Today I Asked: Today I No Longer Feared:

Based On My Response To The   Today It Made Me Feel Good To
Previous Prompt, The Result Was: Complete This Conversation:

I Let Go Of The Fear: Today I Responded The Way My
                                 Spirit Wanted To By:

Today I Set The Boundary:

I Will No Longer Be Silent About The Things That Matter To Me.

Speaking Up Daily

Morning Thoughts

Date:

I Feel:

What Is On My Mind This Morning?

Today I Have Peace In Knowing:

Today I Will Have The Courage To Say:

I Am Declaring:

Evening Thoughts

How Did I Speak Up For Myself Today?

I Feel Good Now That I:

Today I Asked:

Today I No Longer Feared:

Based On My Response To The Previous Prompt, The Result Was:

Today It Made Me Feel Good To Complete This Conversation:

I Let Go Of The Fear:

Today I Responded The Way My Spirit Wanted To By:

Today I Set The Boundary:

Speaking Up Daily

Morning Thoughts

Date:

What Is On My Mind This
Morning?

Today I Will Have The Courage To
Say:

I Feel:

Today I Have Peace In Knowing:

I Am Declaring:

Evening Thoughts

How Did I Speak Up For Myself
Today?

Today I Asked:

Based On My Response To The
Previous Prompt, The Result Was:

I Let Go Of The Fear:

Today I Set The Boundary:

I Feel Good Now That I:

Today I No Longer Feared:

Today It Made Me Feel Good To
Complete This Conversation:

Today I Responded The Way My
Spirit Wanted To By:

Speaking Up Daily

Morning Thoughts

Date: I Feel:

What Is On My Mind This   Today I Have Peace In Knowing:
Morning?

Today I Will Have The Courage To   I Am Declaring:
Say:

Evening Thoughts

How Did I Speak Up For Myself   I Feel Good Now That I:
Today?

Today I Asked: Today I No Longer Feared:

Based On My Response To The   Today It Made Me Feel Good To
Previous Prompt, The Result Was: Complete This Conversation:

I Let Go Of The Fear: Today I Responded The Way My
                                         Spirit Wanted To By:

Today I Set The Boundary:

I Am Not
Afraid To Lose
Anyone Who
Does Not Want
Me To Stand
Up For Me.

My Thoughts Out Loud

Speaking Up Daily

Morning Thoughts

Date:

I Feel:

What Is On My Mind This Morning?

Today I Have Peace In Knowing:

Today I Will Have The Courage To Say:

I Am Declaring:

Evening Thoughts

How Did I Speak Up For Myself Today?

I Feel Good Now That I:

Today I Asked:

Today I No Longer Feared:

Based On My Response To The Previous Prompt, The Result Was:

Today It Made Me Feel Good To Complete This Conversation:

I Let Go Of The Fear:

Today I Responded The Way My Spirit Wanted To By:

Today I Set The Boundary:

Speaking Up Daily

Morning Thoughts

Date: I Feel:

What Is On My Mind This   Today I Have Peace In Knowing:
Morning?

Today I Will Have The Courage To   I Am Declaring:
Say:

Evening Thoughts

How Did I Speak Up For Myself   I Feel Good Now That I:
Today?

Today I Asked: Today I No Longer Feared:

Based On My Response To The   Today It Made Me Feel Good To
Previous Prompt, The Result Was: Complete This Conversation:

I Let Go Of The Fear: Today I Responded The Way My
                                     Spirit Wanted To By:

Today I Set The Boundary:

I Have Found My Voice.

I Like To Keep Saying To Myself....

Speaking Up Daily

Morning Thoughts

Date:

I Feel:

What Is On My Mind This
Morning?

Today I Have Peace In Knowing:

Today I Will Have The Courage To
Say:

I Am Declaring:

Evening Thoughts

How Did I Speak Up For Myself
Today?

I Feel Good Now That I:

Today I Asked:

Today I No Longer Feared:

Based On My Response To The
Previous Prompt, The Result Was:

Today It Made Me Feel Good To
Complete This Conversation:

I Let Go Of The Fear:

Today I Responded The Way My
Spirit Wanted To By:

Today I Set The Boundary:

My Words Are Used To Love Myself And Others.

I Will Face My Fears.

Speaking Up Daily

Morning Thoughts

Date: | I Feel:

What Is On My Mind This Morning?

Today I Have Peace In Knowing:

Today I Will Have The Courage To Say:

I Am Declaring:

Evening Thoughts

How Did I Speak Up For Myself Today?

I Feel Good Now That I:

Today I Asked:

Today I No Longer Feared:

Based On My Response To The Previous Prompt, The Result Was:

Today It Made Me Feel Good To Complete This Conversation:

I Let Go Of The Fear:

Today I Responded The Way My Spirit Wanted To By:

Today I Set The Boundary:

Speaking Up Daily

Morning Thoughts

Date: I Feel:

What Is On My Mind This   Today I Have Peace In Knowing:
Morning?

Today I Will Have The Courage To   I Am Declaring:
Say:

Evening Thoughts

How Did I Speak Up For Myself   I Feel Good Now That I:
Today?

Today I Asked: Today I No Longer Feared:

Based On My Response To The   Today It Made Me Feel Good To
Previous Prompt, The Result Was: Complete This Conversation:

I Let Go Of The Fear: Today I Responded The Way My
                                         Spirit Wanted To By:

Today I Set The Boundary:

Speaking Up Daily

Morning Thoughts

Date: I Feel:

What Is On My Mind This   Today I Have Peace In Knowing:
Morning?

Today I Will Have The Courage To   I Am Declaring:
Say:

Evening Thoughts

How Did I Speak Up For Myself   I Feel Good Now That I:
Today?

Today I Asked: Today I No Longer Feared:

Based On My Response To The   Today It Made Me Feel Good To
Previous Prompt, The Result Was: Complete This Conversation:

I Let Go Of The Fear: Today I Responded The Way My
                                         Spirit Wanted To By:

Today I Set The Boundary:

I Fight For Myself By Speaking Up For Myself And Believing In Myself.

Made in the USA
Middletown, DE
05 September 2021